10·50

James Rae

40 Modern Studies
in Rhythm and Interpretation

40 moderne Rhythmus-
und Interpretationsstudien

for Solo Clarinet
für Klarinette solo

Grades 1 – Diploma

www.**universal**edition.com

vienna · london · new york

UE 19 735
ISMN M-008-04533-2
UPC 8-03452-01128-6
ISBN 978-3-7024-1385-9

CONTENTS/INHALT

Page/Seite

1.	Prowlin'	2
2.	Undercover	2
3.	Sad Dance	3
4.	Jumpin'	3
5.	Backtrack	4
6.	In the Wings	4
7.	Slow Motion	4
8.	The Big One	5
9.	Passing Time	5
10.	Forever	6
11.	Tumbledown Blues	6
12.	In the Beginning	7
13.	Sir Neville	7
14.	Last Chance	8
15.	Ted's Shuffle	9
16.	Happy Ending	9
17.	Movin'	10
18.	Flying Overland	11
19.	Windy Ridge	12
20.	Down to Earth	13
21.	Catch it!	14
22.	Slavonic Dance	15
23.	Dai's Surprise	16
24.	Exclusive	17
25.	Ambiguity	18
26.	On the Brink	19
27.	Now Hear This!	20
28.	In a Dream	21
29.	Helix	22
30.	All Change!	23
31.	Images	24
32.	Latin Jive	25
33.	Round and Round	26
34.	Entanglement	28
35.	Meditation	29
36.	Hard Rock Blues	30
37.	Frenzy	32
38.	Inside – out	34
39.	Nomad	35
40.	Oiled Wheels	36

PREFACE

This book has been written to familiarise the clarinettist with the various rhythms and phrasings encountered in modern music.

Each study deals with a particular aspect of rhythmic playing, ranging from Jazz and Rock to modern Classical interpretation. They are of short to moderate length in order to maximise concentration on style.

The studies have been compiled in order of difficulty to enable the player to gauge his or her progress.

VORWORT

Dieser Band wurde geschrieben, um Klarinettisten mit den verschiedenen Rhythmen und Phrasierungen der modernen Musik vertraut zu machen.

Jede Etüde behandelt einen speziellen Aspekt des rhythmischen Spiels der verschiedensten Stilbereiche, der Jazz und Rockmusik.

Die Etüden sind kurz und nach Schwierigkeitsgraden geordnet. Der Spieler kann sich daher gut auf die einzelnen Stile konzentrieren und seine Fortschritte selbst überprüfen.

James Rae

40 MODERN STUDIES
MODERNE STUDIEN

1 Prowlin'

JAMES RAE

Misterioso

2 Undercover

Steadily

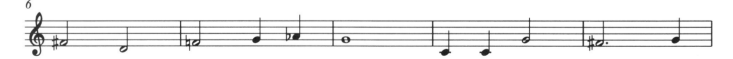

Universal Edition UE 19735

3 Sad Dance

4 Jumpin'

4

5 Backtrack

6 In the Wings

7 Slow Motion

8 The Big One

9 Passing Time

6

10 Forever

11 Tumbledown Blues

12 In the Beginning

13 Sir Neville

8

14 Last Chance

15 Ted's Shuffle

16 Happy Ending

J - 28/1

17 Movin'

Fast swing tempo (♩ = 200) (♫ = ♩³♪)

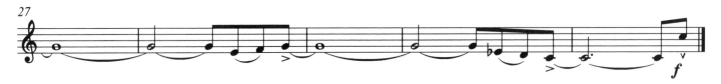

18 Flying Overland

12

19 Windy Ridge

Steady funk tempo (♩ = 100)

UE 19735

20 Down to Earth

UE 19735

21 Catch it!

22 Slavonic Dance

23 Dai's Surprise

24 Exclusive

25 Ambiguity

Joey
23/6

26 On the Brink

UE 19735

27 Now Hear This!

28 In a Dream

29 Helix

30 All Change!

31 Images

32 Latin Jive

33 Round and Round

UE 19735

34 Entanglement

35 Meditation

36 Hard Rock Blues

37 Frenzy

38 Inside-out

39 Nomad

40 Oiled Wheels

Universal Clarinet Edition

UE-Nr.

11 679 **Béla BARTÓK / Zoltán SZÉKELY:** Romanian Folk Dances,
Edition for Clarinet and Piano (Berkes)

14 205 **Richard Rodney BENNETT:** Crosstalk for 2 Clarinets

17 140 **Richard Rodney BENNETT:** Conversations for 2 Clarinets

18 265 **Helmut BORNEFELD:** Little Suite for Clarinet and Keyboard Instrument (Piano / Organ)

19 081 **Bernhard Henrik CRUSELL:** Concerto for Clarinet and Orchestra Op. 1
Edition for Clarinet and Piano (Weston)

19 084 **Bernhard Henrik CRUSELL:** Concerto for Clarinet and Orchestra Op. 5
Edition for Clarinet and Piano (Weston)

18 267 **Bernhard Henrik CRUSELL:** Concerto for Clarinet and Orchestra Op. 11
Edition for Clarinet and Piano (Weston)

17 141 **Joseph KÜFFNER:** 24 Instructional Duets for 2 Clarinets, Op. 200 (Joppig)

18 263 **Felix MENDELSSOHN BARTHOLDY / Pamela WESTON:** Two Songs for 2 Clarinets and Piano

19 086 **W. A. MOZART:** Concerto K 622, Edition for Bassett Horn in A or Clarinet in A (Weston)

18 261 **W. A. MOZART / Georg Friedrich FUCHS:** Airs and Waltzes from 'The Magic Flute'
for 2 Clarinets (Weston)

18 262 **Ignaz J. PLEYEL / GEBAUER:** Six Duets for 2 Clarinets Vol. I (Suppan)

19 080 **Ignaz J. PLEYEL / GEBAUER:** Six Duets for 2 Clarinets Vol. II (Suppan)

18 269 **Franz SCHUBERT / Carl BAERMANN:** Six Songs for Clarinet and Piano (Weston)

17 143 **William O. SMITH:** Jazz Set for 2 Clarinets

18 260 **Anton STADLER:** Duet for 2 Clarinets (Klocker)

18 268 **Klaus Hinrich STAHMER:** Funeral Stele to Erich Arendt for 2 Clarinets (1985)

17 142 **Jenö TAKÁCS:** Five Pieces for 3 Clarinets

18 264 100 Studies for the Clarinet (Joppig / Trier)

This series will be continued / Die Reihe wird fortgesetzt

www.**universal**edition.com
vienna · london · new york

583E / VIII 04